Easy Playalong *Clarinet Solos*
Film Themes

C000001770

Wise Publications
part of The Music Sales Group
London/New York/Paris/Sydney/Copenhagen/Berlin/Madrid/Tokyo

Published by
Wise Publications
14-15 Berners Street, London W1T 3LJ, UK.

Exclusive Distributors:
Music Sales Limited
Distribution Centre, Newmarket Road, Bury St Edmunds, Suffolk IP33 3YB, UK.
Music Sales Pty Limited
120 Rothschild Avenue,
Rosebery, NSW 2018, Australia.

Order No. AM985017
ISBN 1-84609-452-6
This book © Copyright 2006 Wise Publications,
a division of Music Sales Limited.

Arranging and engraving supplied by Camden Music.
Compiled by Nick Crispin.
Cover design by Chloë Alexander.
Printed in the EU.

CD recorded, mixed and mastered by Jonas Persson.
Instrumental solos by John Whelan.
New backing tracks arranged by Paul Honey.
Melody line arrangements by Christopher Hussey.

Your Guarantee of Quality
As publishers, we strive to produce every book to the highest commercial standards.
The music has been freshly engraved and the book has been carefully designed to minimise
awkward page turns and to make playing from it a real pleasure.
Particular care has been given to specifying acid-free, neutral-sized paper made from pulps
which have not been elemental chlorine bleached. This pulp is from farmed sustainable forests
and was produced with special regard for the environment.
Throughout, the printing and binding have been planned to ensure a sturdy, attractive
publication which should give years of enjoyment.
If your copy fails to meet our high standards, please inform us and we will gladly replace it.

www.musicsales.com

FREE bonus material downloadable to your computer.
Visit: www.hybridpublications.com
Registration is free and easy.
Your registration code is: HG199

Clarinet
Fingering Chart

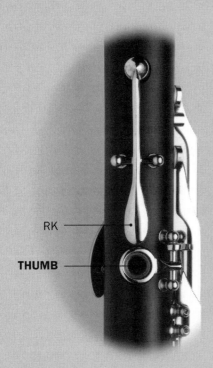

RK

THUMB

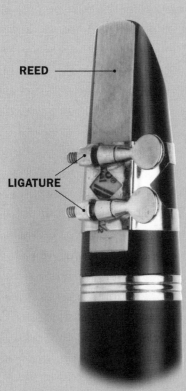

REED

LIGATURE

Mouthpiece

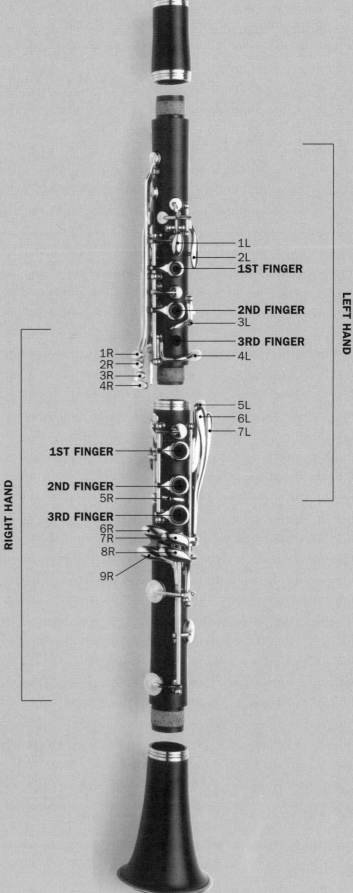

1L
2L
1ST FINGER

2ND FINGER
3L

3RD FINGER
4L

1R
2R
3R
4R

LEFT HAND

5L
6L
7L

1ST FINGER

RIGHT HAND

2ND FINGER
5R

3RD FINGER
6R
7R
8R
9R

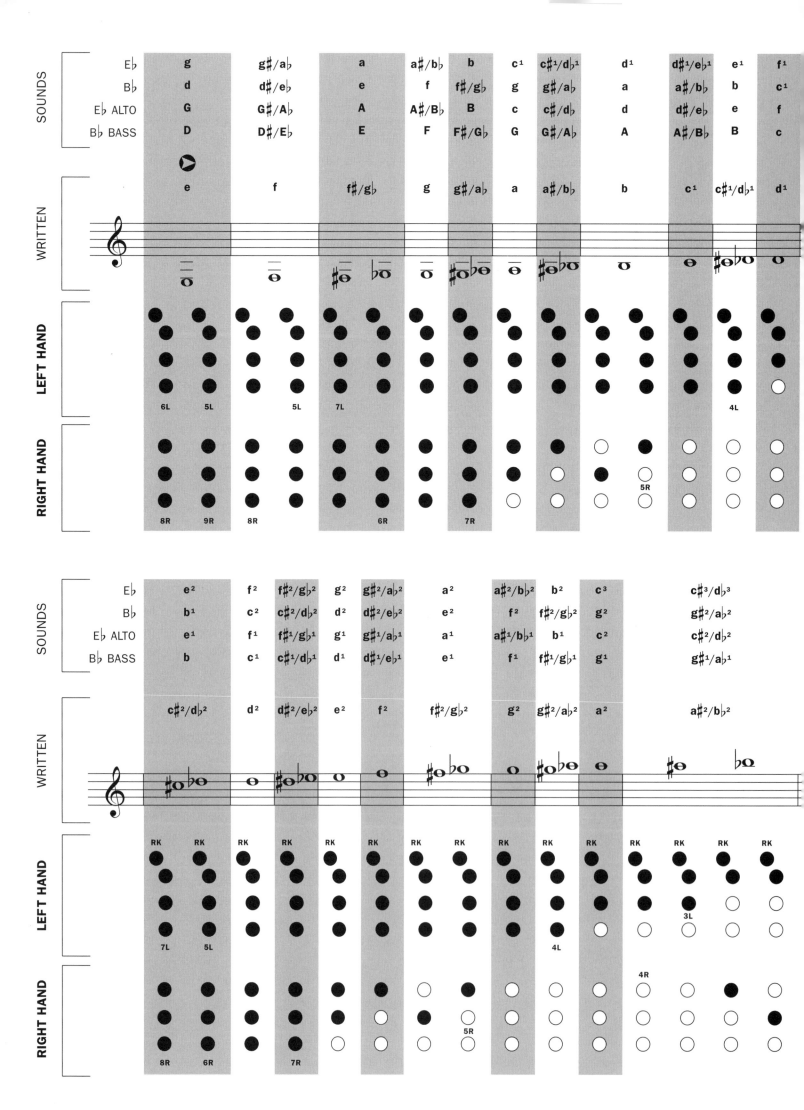

Indicates the lower limit of the best playing range for E♭, B♭, E♭ Alto and B♭ Bass Clarinets

Indicates the upper limit of the best playing range for E♭ and B♭ Clarinets

Indicates the upper limit of the best playing range for E♭ Alto and B♭ Bass Clarinets

PERFORMANCE TIPS

Welcome to this exciting collection of playalong tunes from some of your favourite movies!

Before you begin to play, make sure your instrument is in tune (there are tuning notes on Track 1 of the CD) and listen to the demonstration performances on Tracks 2–11 while following along with the music.

Throughout the book, you'll notice some tiny notes written into the music—these are called **cues**, and they are not to be played. They show you what is happening on the backing track (i.e. what the other instruments are playing) so that you will know when to come in.

Below are some suggestions that will help you improve your performance, including practice tips, handy 'shortcuts' to simplify the music while you are learning it, and some hints that will make it easier to fit your performance to the CD accompaniment.

ANOTHER BEAR (from 'Finding Neverland')

- You will need to count carefully throughout this quirky tune, as the melodic phrases vary in length. Play them as lyrically as possible and you will find that they flow quite naturally.

- In bars 4 and 50, at the start of the tune, don't be thrown off by the accordion, which plays a similar tune but starts slightly later—begin with confidence!

- In the staccato passages (bars 93–99, 102–105 and 115–116) tongue the notes separately and make them as short as possible. To master this technique, practise the staccato passage below:

- The melodic pattern in bars 93–94 is repeated in bars 95–96, and again in bars 98–99. However, it doesn't always begin on the same beat of the bar, so count carefully!

CIRCLE OF LIFE (from 'The Lion King')

- An important feature of this popular song is **syncopation**. A syncopated rhythm occurs when beats of the bar which are normally unaccented are given an accent. The syncopated rhythm first appears in bar 9:

The syncopation occurs on the 'and' of the 2nd beat, which would normally be unaccented. Practise this passage until you are confident with the rhythm and you'll find the song much easier to master. Also, count very carefully during bar 10 to make sure you don't miss the last quaver, which is an upbeat to the next bar.

- The chorus begins just before the double barline at bar 25. Practise the rhythm in bar 24, counting carefully in order to master the syncopated quaver–crotchet–quaver rhythm on beats 3 and 4, as this will return later on:

E.T. THE EXTRA-TERRESTRIAL (Main Theme)

- This classic film theme is a bit challenging, but once you've mastered it you will find it great fun to play! Start by practising the main theme in bars 5–12—once you've learned this, you'll be well on your way:

The 'new' tune that begins in bar 13 is not really new at all—it's the main theme with a slight alteration (the semiquaver figure on beat 3 is turned upside down!). Practise this a few times so you can hear the difference:

- You will be playing an **accompaniment** in bars 25–29 and bars 38–50, to go along with the melody on the backing track. These passages can be left out at first, while you are mastering the main tune.

- The fast passages in bars 65–66 might look difficult, but they are simply C major scales starting on G, played staccato.

- Listen to the ending (from bar 68) a few times before you try to play it. Listen carefully to the **cues**, which will help you fit your performance to the backing track.

THE GODFATHER (Main Theme)

- There are several accidentals to watch out for in this tune, such as the E♭ in bar 14 and the G#s in bars 16 and 18. Remember that they only affect the notes in the bar in which they appear. So, for example, after having played G# in bars 16 and 18, the G in bar 20 is natural again (you'll see a natural sign ♮ in brackets to remind you). Note that the **'middle 8'** (the middle eight bars of the tune, from bar 24 to bar 31) includes two accidentals: A♭ in bar 24 and E♭ in bar 30.

- Practise the leap from E down to G# in bar 22, which occurs again later on:

- The passage in bars 57–64 is a **countermelody**. This is a secondary melody that serves as an accompaniment to the main tune, which is played on the backing track. If you find this difficult, you might want to leave it out while you master the rest of the tune, and then return to it later. If you decide to leave it out, then you must rest through this section and begin again with the 'middle 8' tune on the second beat of bar 64.

- From bar 88 to the end there is a sign **'Optional 8va'** followed by a broken line. This indicates that you can play this passage an octave higher if you are daring enough!

THE HEART ASKS PLEASURE FIRST (from 'The Piano')

- You may find the rhythm of this tune a bit challenging at first. Here are the first four bars you play:

Each bar contains three crotchet beats, or six quaver beats. Try counting it in quavers first (as shown beneath the stave in the example above) until you can feel where the second note falls. The $\frac{3}{4}$ rhythm is written out above the stave, showing you how you would count it in crotchets.

- The little lines below (and sometimes above) the notes are called **tenuto** marks. These marks indicate that you should hold the notes for their full written duration and tongue them more than you would normally, so that they are slightly accented.

- You'll notice that the tune is made up of very long phrases, and there is not much time to breathe! The ticks ✓ suggest suitable places for you to take quick breaths. To make it easier while you are learning the music, you could make the note before the breathmark shorter in length to give you more time to breathe. For example:

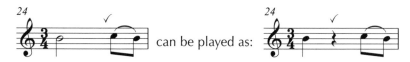

JURASSIC PARK (Main Theme)

- Count very carefully during the introduction, as the time signature changes a number of times before settling into $\frac{4}{4}$ at bar 10. Watch out especially for the extra beat in the $\frac{5}{4}$ bar (bar 5).

- The tempo almost doubles at bar 10. To find your new tempo, listen carefully to the harp part, which is in fast crotchets underneath your held semibreve:

- As you become more confident with the tune, make sure you observe the dynamics, with particular attention to the **hairpins** (e.g. in bars 21–26) which indicate a crescendo ⦤ and a diminuendo ⦥ . These will help you give character and shape to the melody.

- For a strong ending, you will need to play the last four notes (bars 72–78) very confidently! Count steadily and listen to the five harp notes in bars 76–77, which will lead you right to your final note.

MOON RIVER (from 'Breakfast At Tiffany's')

- This song should be played with a tender tone and in a **legato** (smooth) manner. The tune is quite straightforward, following very closely to the major scale and arpeggio, but there are a few surprises! Watch for the leap of nearly an octave between G and the higher F#, which happens in the melody several times (for example, in bars 12–13, and in bar 40, where it is very quick):

- There is an instrumental section in bars 47–62, during which you play an accompanying countermelody. Watch for the key change to C major, and the accidentals in bars 54–56 and 61–62:

> If you find this section too difficult when you are beginning to learn the piece, you can leave it out and replace it with rests (returning with the tune in bar 63).

MY HEART WILL GO ON (from 'Titanic')

- The biggest challenge you will face in this famous song is the key change at bar 53, taking you from F major with one flat (B♭) to A major, which has three sharps (F#, C# and G#). Remember that in A major the Bs are no longer flat, but natural. It might be helpful to write the sharp sign (#) in pencil in front of all Fs, Cs and Gs from bar 53 to the end of the song so that you don't forget.

- Watch out for the syncopated notes, which are 'pushed' (ie. they happen just before the beat). Have a look at bar 27:

> This also occurs in bars 35, 55 and 63.

- Just as you did in 'Circle of Life,' you will need to repeat the first part of this song (ie. you'll play the first part twice before moving on). At bar 41 onward, you'll notice **1st time bar** and **2nd time bar** symbols. Make sure that when you get to bar 41 you are ready to go back to bar 9 and repeat what you have already played. Then, on the second time through, you should go straight to the '2nd time bar' once you've played bar 40. Notice also that you should play with a different dynamic on the repeat: *mf* rather than *p*.

- The last note of the song, A, is held for 10 written beats. As there is a **fermata** ⌒ (pause mark) over the last, tied semibreve, this note needs to be held for even longer than written. Therefore, you need to take an extra big breath at the tick ✓ in the middle of bar 78. Fortunately, there is a diminuendo hairpin to *pp* (pianissimo = very soft), so you can use that big breath very slowly!

INTO THE WEST (from 'The Lord Of The Rings: The Return Of The King')

- Listen carefully to the harp part at the beginning of this song, and count along. This will help you feel the tempo and know where to come in.

- Be aware of the **syncopated** rhythms, where the notes are 'pushed' to begin on the offbeat, just before they would normally begin. These 'pushes' feature in bars 10 and 16, but let's take a closer look at bars 23–25 in particular. The basic tune, without the 'pushes,' is this:

With the syncopation added, we get the following (the 'pushed' notes are in boxes):

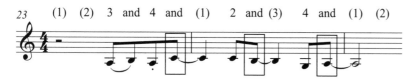

- Make sure you practise the articulation of the figure beginning at bar 21—the tonguing is indicated above the stave:

YOU'VE GOT A FRIEND IN ME (from 'Toy Story')

- This fun song is played with a **swing** feel—once you have mastered this, you will find that playing in this style is very natural and fun!

  At the top you'll see the following marking:

  This means that all dotted quaver–semiquaver rhythms  should be played as:

  Practise the figure in bars 6–7, since this rhythm occurs many times throughout the song, and 'swing' the figure on the second beat:

 becomes:

- Notice the accent marks in bars 11, 15 and 24. These notes should be tongued harder than usual so they stand out:

- Finally, be aware of the accidentals in bars 31–32:

Another Bear
(from 'Finding Neverland')

Composed by Jan A.P. Kaczmarek

With a lilt ♩ = 126

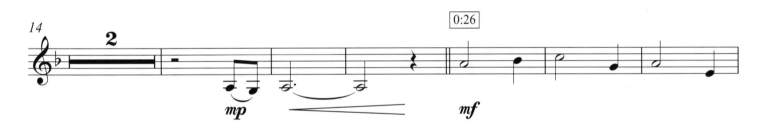

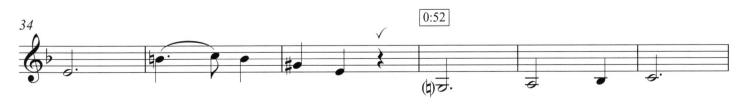

Circle Of Life

(from Walt Disney Pictures' 'The Lion King')

Music by Elton John & Words by Tim Rice

With a slow and steady beat ♩ = 88

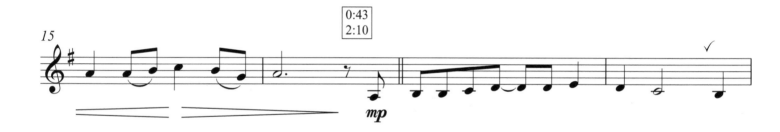

E.T. The Extra-Terrestrial
(Main Theme)

Composed by John Williams

The Godfather
(Main Theme)

Words by Larry Kusik & Music by Nino Rota

18

The Heart Asks Pleasure First
(from 'The Piano')

Composed by Michael Nyman

Jurassic Park
(Main Theme)

Composed by John Williams

Moon River
(from 'Breakfast At Tiffany's')

Words by Johnny Mercer & Music by Henry Mancini

My Heart Will Go On
(Love Theme from 'Titanic')

Words by Will Jennings & Music by James Horner

Soulfully and expressively ♩ = 98

Into The West

(from 'The Lord Of The Rings: The Return Of The King')

Words & Music by Annie Lennox, Howard Shore & Fran Walsh

You've Got A Friend In Me
(from 'Toy Story')

Words & Music by Randy Newman

With a bouncy swing ♩ = 116

(strings/voices)

0:38

1 2 3 4 5 6 7 8 9

CD Track Listing

1 Tuning notes

Full instrumental performances...

2 Another Bear *from* **'Finding Neverland'**
(Kaczmarek) Sony/ATV Music Publishing (UK) Limited.

3 Circle Of Life *from* **Walt Disney Pictures' 'The Lion King'**
(John/Rice) Warner/Chappell Artemis Music.

4 E.T. The Extra-Terrestrial (Main Theme) *from* **'E.T. The Extra-Terrestrial'**
(Williams) Universal/MCA Music Limited.

5 The Godfather (Main Theme) *from* **'The Godfather'**
(Kusik/Rota) Famous Music Publishing Limited.

6 The Heart Asks Pleasure First *from* **'The Piano'**
(Nyman) Chester Music Limited.

7 Jurassic Park (Main Theme) *from* **'Jurassic Park'**
(Williams) Universal/MCA Music Limited.

8 Moon River *from* **'Breakfast At Tiffany's'**
(Mercer/Mancini) Famous Music Publishing Limited.

9 My Heart Will Go On (Love Theme) *from* **'Titanic'**
(Jennings/Horner) Rondor Music (London) Limited/EMI Music Publishing Limited.

10 Into The West *from* **'The Lord Of The Rings: The Return Of The King'**
(Lennox/Shore/Walsh) Sony/ATV Music Publishing (UK) Limited/Warner/Chappell Music Limited/BMG Music Publishing Limited.

11 You've Got A Friend In Me *from* **'Toy Story'**
(Newman) Warner/Chappell Music Limited.

Backing tracks only...

12 Another Bear *from* **'Finding Neverland'**
13 Circle Of Life *from* **Walt Disney Pictures' 'The Lion King'**
14 E.T. The Extra-Terrestrial (Main Theme) *from* **'E.T. The Extra-Terrestrial'**
15 The Godfather (Main Theme) *from* **'The Godfather'**
16 The Heart Asks Pleasure First *from* **'The Piano'**
17 Jurassic Park (Main Theme) *from* **'Jurassic Park'**
18 Moon River *from* **'Breakfast At Tiffany's'**
19 My Heart Will Go On (Love Theme) *from* **'Titanic'**
20 Into The West *from* **'The Lord Of The Rings: The Return Of The King'**
21 You've Got A Friend In Me *from* **'Toy Story'**

To remove your CD from the plastic sleeve, lift the small lip to break the perforations. Replace the disc after use for convenient storage.